The Greek Heroes

Simplified by Michael West
Revised by D K Swan

Illustrated by Anthony Colbert

Longman

850 word
vocabulary

Longman Group Limited
Longman House, Burnt Mill, Harlow,
Essex CM20 2JE, England
and Associated Companies throughout the World.

First published 1955
New Edition 1980
Fourth impression 1985

ISBN 0 582 52677 9

Acknowledgement
Cover photograph by M. Chuzeville
and supplied by the Musée du Louvre

Produced by Longman Group (FE) Ltd
Printed in Hong Kong

Contents

Words outside Stage 2 of the New Method
Supplementary Readers are in a list on page 74.

Perseus and the head of Medusa

The two princes

Argos was a beautiful country, but its people were not happy. Two princes ruled it, and they hated each other. Their names were Acrisius and Proetus.

Acrisius had a daughter, Danae, but he had no sons. He wanted a son, and he wanted that son to rule Argos. So he went to a wise man.

'The gods are angry,' the wise man said, 'because you hate your brother. You will not have a son. Your daughter, Danae, will have a son, and he will kill you.'

Acrisius thought, 'Danae must not have a son.' And he locked her in a room with strong stone walls, and with only a small opening for light and air. 'Now she can't have a son,' he said to himself.

But no one can beat the gods, and the great god Zeus himself visited Danae. He came through the small opening as a stream of golden light.

The son of Danae

After a time, Danae had a son. He was a beautiful child. She called him Perseus.

Then Acrisius said, 'If that child becomes a man, he will kill me. So he and his mother must not live.'

Acrisius did not dare to kill his own daughter. But he put Danae and her child in a strong wooden case. Then he put the case into the sea.

'I'll never see them again,' he thought.

The sea carried the case to an island far away— the island of Seriphos. There, an old man had come down to the sea to get fish. His name was Dictys, and he was the brother of Polydectes, the king of Seriphos.

Dictys saw the case in the sea. 'What is that?' he wondered. 'A big case in the sea!' He brought it to land and began to open it. 'There is something in it—a woman! A beautiful woman and a child! They are alive!'

Dictys took Danae and her son out of the case. He took them to his home. Danae and her son lived there for fifteen years.

Athene

When he was fifteen years old, Perseus was very big and strong. He was very beautiful too.

People said, 'He is like a god: he is so strong and so beautiful.'

Perseus became a seaman and went away on a ship. The ship was away for a long time. It visited very many Greek cities and islands.

On one of the islands, Perseus went to sleep at the foot of a great tree. In his sleep he saw a beautiful woman.

'Who are you?' he asked.

'I am the goddess Athene. I know what men think. Even if they try to hide their thoughts, I see inside them. I know those who are strong and those who are not. Do you want to be great and to work for me and do what I say?'

'Yes,' said Perseus, 'I want to be great. Will you help me to do great things?'

Perseus sees Medusa's face

Athene had a shield on her arm. 'Look in my shield,' she said to Perseus. 'Tell me what you see.'

Perseus saw in the bright shield a terrible face. It was the face of a woman, but it was ugly and bad, and on the woman's head there were snakes.

'That's a terrible sight,' he said. 'Somebody ought to kill her.'

Athene answered, 'That's the face of Medusa.

You must kill Medusa, and I will help you. But first you must go home and do the work there that you have to do. I will come to you again.'

He looked up, but Athene had gone. There was no one near him.

Danae in the king's house

When Perseus went away, King Polydectes made the beautiful Danae go and live in his house. He wanted her to marry him, but she would not. So he made her work as a servant. She brought water from the river; she washed the floors; she washed clothes; she brought food to the table. 'When she is tired of this work, she will marry me,' he hoped.

Perseus came home. He went to Dictys and said, 'Where is my mother?'

Dictys was very sad. 'Polydectes took her,' he said. 'I couldn't save her. He has made her a servant in his house.'

'A servant! My mother a servant! That's terrible!' And Perseus ran to the king's palace.

A soldier at the door cried, 'Stop! You can't go in.' Perseus threw the man down quite easily and went into the house.

He found his mother washing the floor in a room at the back of the house. He took her hand and led her into the great hall, where

Polydectes was sitting.

Perseus said to the king, 'You have made my mother a servant! I shall kill you for that!'

Dictys ran into the hall. 'No, Perseus!' he cried. 'No! He is my brother. Don't kill him. I saved you from the sea: now I ask you to save him. Don't kill my brother!'

'Because you ask me, I won't kill him. He shall live.' And Perseus took his mother away.

There was a house of the goddess Athene on the island. He put his mother in it. Perseus and Dictys went to see her every day.

'*What will you give me?*'

Polydectes still wanted the beautiful Danae, but he couldn't take her away from the house of Athene.

He thought, 'I must send Perseus away. I can't get Danae when he is here.' He thought again: 'Ah! I know what I must do.'

On one day in each year, all the rich men went to the king's house, and each man gave him some beautiful or useful thing. One man gave Polydectes a horse; another gave him a beautiful coat; another man gave him a box made of gold; another gave him a jewel.

Perseus went with the other men to the king's house, but he had nothing to give. He was not rich: he had come to Seriphos as a child in a case, and he had no house, no gold—nothing.

Polydectes said, 'Perseus, I am your king. I have asked you to my house on my great day. All the other men have given me something. What will you give me?'

Then all the rich men laughed. They hated the beautiful young man. They said, 'This man was thrown up by the sea. He has nothing. Why is he here? He can't give anything to the king. Will you give Polydectes six eggs, or some flowers, Perseus?' And they all laughed again.

Perseus said, 'I will bring something that no other man can bring. What do you want, Polydectes?'

Polydectes knew that Medusa was the most terrible of all living things. 'You will bring me whatever I want?' he asked. 'Then bring me the head of Medusa.'

The king and all the rich men laughed at this.

Perseus didn't laugh. 'I'll bring it,' he said.

'Go, then,' said Polydectes. 'Come back when you have got it.' The king knew that any man who looked at the face of Medusa was changed into stone. 'He'll never come back,' he thought. 'Perseus will go, because he is brave. He will become a stone, and we won't see him again.'

Athene and Hermes

Perseus went and stood by the sea. 'Polydectes is happy,' he thought. 'He wanted me to say that. No one will save my mother from him while I am away. I have been foolish. O Athene, help me! Tell me what I must do now.'

Perseus saw a bright light far away over the sea. It was like a small sun, and he couldn't look at it. He shut his eyes.

'You can open your eyes now,' a voice said.

Athene was standing in front of him, with her bright shield on her arm. At her side there was a person whose eyes were as bright as stars. In his hand he had a shining sword, and on his feet there were golden shoes, and the shoes had wings. It was the god Hermes.

'Take this shield'

Athene said, 'Perseus, you are strong. You are a man. You were not afraid of the king. Are you afraid to kill Medusa and cut off her head?'

'What is Medusa?' Perseus asked.

'Medusa was once a beautiful woman, but she did a terrible thing, so the gods changed her into a Gorgon. There are snakes on her head, and her hands are like the feet of a great bird. Her face is terrible: any man who looks at it is

changed to stone. Many men have gone to kill
Medusa the Gorgon; none of them has come
back. They are stones—dead stones—standing
in the place where they looked at her face.'

'Can *I* kill Medusa?' asked Perseus. 'Or will
I too become a stone when I look at her?'

'Take this shield,' said Athene. 'When you
come near her, do not look straight at her. Look
at her only in this shield. When you have cut
off her head, put it in a cloth so that it cannot
be seen.—But think before you go out to kill
Medusa. She lives very far away. You will go
far over land and sea. You must go over the
country of the dead. Many men have died
there, and no one has ever found them.'

'Go north—north—north'

'Where is the country of the dead, and where
is Medusa? How can I go across the seas to
reach her?' asked Perseus.

'Go north—north—north,' said Athene.
'There, in the far north, you will find the Three
Sisters who have only one eye. Say to them,
"Where are the Daughters of Night who sit near
the golden tree?" Only the Three Sisters can tell
you where they live. Then go on—on—on, and
find the Daughters of Night. Say to the
Daughters of Night, "Where is Medusa the

Gorgon?" They can tell you where she is.'

'How can I go across the sea?' asked Perseus. 'I have no boat.'

Then Hermes, who was standing near Athene, said, 'Take these wings. Put them on your feet. They will carry you over the sea. Take this sword. It will cut off the head of Medusa the Gorgon.'

Perseus flies

Perseus asked one more question: 'Shall I first go to my mother and Dictys and tell them that I am going?'

'No,' said Athene. 'I will tell them. Come with me now.'

They went up to the top of a hill. Then Perseus put Hermes' wings on his feet and took Hermes' sword.

'Jump off the top of this hill,' said Athene. 'The wings will carry you. You won't fall into the sea.'

Perseus looked down. He saw the sea far, far down. 'I mustn't be afraid,' he thought. He shut his eyes and jumped. The wings carried him up and up. He looked back and saw Athene and Hermes far under him, very small and bright on the hilltop.

The Three Sisters

Perseus went north—north—north, over the sea. He came to the country of the dead, where there is no water and there are no trees and no living things.

At last he came to the far north, where the Three Sisters were sitting near a fire. They had only one eye. The first sister looked at Perseus with it; then she gave the eye to her sister. The second sister put the eye in her head and looked. Then she gave the eye to the third sister, and she put the eye in her head and looked at Perseus.

Perseus said, 'Sisters, you are old and you know many things. Tell me, Old Sisters, where I can find the Daughters of Night.'

Then the first sister said, 'Who calls us old? Who is this who calls us old?'

The second sister said, 'Is it a man? Give me the eye.' She looked. 'Yes, it is a man,' she said. 'We do not love men. Men are bad. We will tell him nothing.'

The third sister said, 'We will tell him nothing, but give me the eye.'

Perseus takes the eye

When the second sister took the eye out of her

head, Perseus moved quickly near to her. He put out his hand, and the second sister put the eye into it. She thought that she was putting the eye into her sister's hand, but it was the hand of Perseus.

Then Perseus said, 'Tell me now. Where can I find the Daughters of Night? I have your eye in my hand. Tell me—or I will throw your eye into the fire, and you will never see again.'

They did not answer.

'Tell me! Quickly!—If I throw it into the fire, or if I throw it into the water, you will never see again.'

Then they said, 'Give us the eye. We will tell you.'

'No,' Perseus said. 'Tell me first. Then I will give you your eye.'

'You must go south,' said the first sister. 'Go to the far south. You will come to a great mountain—Mount Atlas. Near the mountain there is a beautiful garden. In that garden there is a tree with golden apples on it. The Daughters of Night sit near the golden apple tree.'

The Daughters of Night

Perseus went up—far up—over the great sea. He flew on—and on. The sun was hot, and the sea was bright. He went down, flying near the water like a bird. At last, he saw a very high mountain. There were trees and flowers at the foot of the mountain, and there was a river, very bright in the sun. But there were no houses and no fields. No people lived there.

Perseus came down. He walked through a beautiful garden, and he heard singing. Three women were singing in the garden, and the birds sang with them. It was a very beautiful sound.

The Daughters of Night heard him coming to the place. They stopped singing. He came out from the trees, and he saw them and the golden apple tree.

'Who are you?' asked one of the Daughters of Night. 'Are you a thief? Have you come to take our golden apples?'

'No,' said Perseus. 'I'm not a thief. I don't want your golden apples. I want to know where I can find Medusa the Gorgon. I'm going to kill her. Tell me where I can find her.'

'We won't tell you now,' she said. 'Come and play with us. We have lived here for thousands of years, and no one has come. We sit here singing, and there is no one to sing with us. We play, but there is no one to play with us.'

'I must not play here,' said Perseus. 'I must go on and kill Medusa. Tell me where she is.'

'She will change you to stone,' she said. 'Why

do you want to die and be changed to stone?'

'Athene is helping me. She has given me her shield, and I have the sword of Hermes. So I won't die.'

'If Medusa sees you, she will change you into stone. You must have the Coat of Night. She won't see you in that. No one can see you. So the Coat of Night will save you.'

The Coat of Night

'Where is the Coat of Night?' Perseus asked. 'Can I get it?'

'I'll bring it to you, but it is far away. Wait here for seven days. I'll come back and give it to you then.'

So Perseus was in the garden for seven days. He sat near the golden apple tree, playing and singing with the other Daughters of Night. Then the third sister came back, after seven days, bringing the Coat of Night.

Perseus was standing near the river, and he could see his face in the water.

'Now put on the coat,' said the Daughter of Night.

He put on the coat, and he looked in the water. He saw nothing! He couldn't see his face in the water. No one could see him because he was wearing the Coat of Night.

Then the Daughters of Night said, 'Atlas is our father's brother. We'll go up to the top of the mountain, and Atlas will show you the island where Medusa lives.'

They went up to the top of the mountain where Atlas lived.

Atlas said, 'I can see over all countries. I can see the island where Medusa lives. I can see her and her two sisters: she is asleep and her sisters are sleeping near her.' Then he told Perseus how to find the island.

Perseus thanked the Daughters of Night. They were very sad because he was going away, but they gave him the Coat of Night. He put it on, and then he flew up—up—and on to the island of Medusa.

The Gorgon's head

He flew over a sea where there were no ships, over countries where there were no people. Then he looked down at an island. He saw two big forms on the rocks near the sea—Medusa's sisters.

Perseus came down on to the island. He looked in Athene's shield. In the shield he saw the Gorgons sleeping near the sea. He saw Medusa. She had snakes for hair, and her hands were like the feet of a great bird. She was a

terrible sight.

Perseus took the sword in his hand. Then, looking in the shield, he cut off her head. He put the head in a cloth, and flew up with it. He flew up and up. But the two sisters had heard him. They gave a terrible cry and came up with their great wings to catch him as he flew away with the wings of Hermes on his feet.

They could hear him, but they couldn't see him because he was wearing the Coat of Night. He flew up and up, but the Gorgons came nearer and nearer.

He went down, down near the sea, where the waves ran up on to the rocks. The Gorgons heard the sea, but they could not hear Perseus because of the waves. They flew north and south and east and west, but they could not hear him. They went up; he was not there. They went down; and they heard the sea on the rocks.

Perseus flew on.

Athene helps Perseus again

Perseus flew back to go to his home. He flew over mountains and rivers and great forests. He flew on and on, until he couldn't fly any more. He couldn't go on. He came down in a place where there was no water. There were no trees;

there were no living things. He was in the country of the dead.

'I shall die,' Perseus thought. 'There's no water here, and there's no food. I can't go on.' And he said, 'O Athene, help me! I can't go on.'

The great Athene heard him. Suddenly Perseus saw a little river where there was no river before. And there were trees with fruit on them. So he ate and drank, and thanked Athene. Then he went on, over the sea.

Perseus flew all night over the sea. In the morning he looked down, and he saw mountains and great black rocks near the sea. On one of the rocks there was a woman. She was chained down to the rock.

He flew down. As he came near, he thought, 'This is the most beautiful woman that I have ever seen.' He came down to her and asked, 'Who are you? And why are you chained to this rock?'

Andromeda

'My name is Andromeda,' she said. 'My father is the king of this country. He said, "Andromeda is the most beautiful of all women, more beautiful than a goddess." Poseidon, the sea-god, heard him and said, "She is not more beautiful than my sea-goddesses." So Poseidon made the waters of the sea come up over our country, and then he sent a terrible dragon which comes up out of the water and eats men. And Poseidon said to my father, "Give your daughter to the dragon. The dragon will eat her, and then the water will go back from your country, and the dragon won't come any more." My father, the king, said, "No! I will not give my daughter to the dragon." But the people of the country said, "Our fields are covered with water. The dragon is killing men and women and children. You must do what Poseidon says." They came to my father's house and took me and chained me to this rock. Now the dragon will come.— It is coming now! Look!'

Perseus looked over the sea. He saw a terrible head coming out of the water. It was coming nearer—nearer.

Quickly, he took Hermes' sword. It cut through the chains, and Andromeda stood up.

'Put your hands over your eyes,' said Perseus. 'Don't look.'

The dragon came nearer. Perseus held up the head of Medusa. The dragon looked at it— and was changed into a great black stone. The Dragon Rock is still there now, and people go to see it and remember the story.

Andromeda goes with Perseus

Then Perseus took Andromeda in his arms, and he flew up and on, over fields and houses until he came to her father's palace.

The king sat with his queen in the hall. The queen was crying: 'Oh, my daughter! My beautiful daughter! I shall never see her again. The dragon will kill her.'

The king sat at her side, sadly, with his head in his hands.

The door of the hall opened, and Perseus came in—with Andromeda. Her mother and father couldn't believe it! They were very happy. The king said to Perseus, 'You shall be king of this country, and Andromeda shall be your queen. Stay here with us.'

But Perseus answered, 'I thank you, but I must go back to see my mother. I want to take your daughter with me.'

'Yes,' Andromeda said. 'Where you go, I will go. Your country shall be my country.'

That night, Athene came to Perseus as he was sleeping. She said, 'You have done great things, and I am very pleased. You don't need the wings and the sword and the Coat of Night now, so I will take them. But you will need the Gorgon's head—the head of Medusa. Take it with you.'

In the morning, the sword, the coat and the wings had gone.

Perseus and Andromeda went in a ship, back to the country where his mother was.

They went to see Danae, his mother, and Dictys, his old friend.

'Look at it!'

Then Perseus went to see Polydectes. He carried with him the Gorgon's head in its cloth.

The king was sitting at the table in his hall. All his great men were with him, eating and drinking. Perseus opened the door and went in.

When the king saw Perseus, he cried, 'You have come back, have you? You couldn't get the head of Medusa. So now I shall kill you.'

Perseus took the cloth off the Gorgon's head. 'Look!' he said. 'Look at it! Here is the head of Medusa.'

Polydectes and his great men looked at the terrible head. They could not shut their eyes. They could not stand or run away. They were changed to stones. The table had stone men sitting round it, and at the end of the table sat a stone king.

Perseus made Dictys king of Seriphos. Then he said, 'Good Dictys, I thank you for all that you have done for my mother and for me. Now

I must go back to Argos. That is my mother's country, and it is my country. Danae's father Acrisius is king there, and I must help him.'

Perseus at Larissa

Perseus and Andromeda went on a ship. The ship went first to a town called Larissa.

King Acrisius was in Larissa; he had gone there to visit the king of Larissa, and to see the Games there. When Perseus heard that Acrisius was at the Games, he said to Andromeda, 'I won't tell anyone my name. I won't say who I am until I have won the crown for the best runner, jumper and discus-thrower.'

So Perseus went with the other young men to the Games. Everyone looked at him, and they said, 'Who is this man? He looks very strong— stronger than any man we have ever seen. Who is this unknown man?'

In all the running, Perseus came first; all the others were far behind. In the jumping, no one could jump as far as Perseus. He was first in all the games. The last of the games was throwing the discus. Each man had to throw the heavy round stone as far as he could.

The death of Acrisius

Perseus saw his grandfather watching the Games, and he thought, 'He is very old, but he looks like a king. He doesn't look like a bad man. I'll win the crown, and then I'll put it down at his feet and say, "I am the son of Danae. I want to come home with you to Argos."' He did not know about the wise man who had said to Acrisius, 'Your daughter, Danae, will have a son, and he will kill you.'

Perseus threw the discus and it went high and very far. No one had ever thrown it so far. All the people shouted, 'Good! Good! Throw it again! We want to see how far you can throw.'

He took the discus again and threw it. It flew up—up—up. But it didn't fly straight. It turned in the air—turned towards the place where the king of Larissa was sitting with Acrisius and the other great men. As if the gods were sending it there, the discus turned to hit Acrisius. He fell down and lay there—dead. The gods had punished Acrisius for hating his brother.

Perseus went back to Argos with Andromeda, and he became king. He was a very good king. They lived for many years, and when they died, Athene took them up and made them into stars. Look up at night and you will see Perseus and Andromeda among the stars.

Theseus and the Labyrinth

The great stone

Aegeus was king in Athens. His queen was the beautiful Aethra, but Aegeus left her at Troezen in her father's country.

Before he left her, Aegeus said, 'You are going to have a son. I want to see him only if he is strong and brave. If he can move the rock of Zeus with his hands, he will find things under it. Let him bring those things to me in Athens.'

Aethra did have a son. She called him Theseus, but she didn't tell him his father's name.

When Theseus was fifteen years old, his mother led him to the great stone, the rock of Zeus.

'Move the stone,' she said, 'and bring me the things you find under it.'

Theseus put his hands under the stone, but he couldn't move it: it was too heavy. He went back to his mother and said, 'I can't do it. The stone is too big.'

The sword and the shoes

During the next three years, Theseus became a very strong man. He ran over the hills; he rode horses; no one in the country was as strong as Theseus. Men said, 'He's the strongest man we have ever seen.'

When Theseus was eighteen years old, his mother said, 'Now you can move the stone, and you will know who you are.'

So Theseus went and put his hands under the stone.

'Up! Up!' he said, but it didn't move. He said, 'I'm a man, and I'm strong. It *must* move. I'm going to move it.'

Then he tried again. He threw the stone over on to its side. Then he looked in the hole under it. He saw a sword and two golden shoes. He took them out of the hole and brought them to his mother.

Theseus sets out to go to Athens

Aethra said, 'Now come with me to a place where we can look out over the sea.'

They stood and looked out across the sea, and Aethra said, 'Do you see that country very far away? It is like a little line on the water as far as your eyes can see.'

'Yes,' said Theseus. 'I see it.'

'That,' she said, 'is Attica. Its hills are covered with flowers. Its fields are rich. Birds sing all day in its forests. There are beautiful houses and gardens. What must the king of such a beautiful country do?'

'You have taught me that, mother. He must be a very good king. He must make his people happy. He must think all the time of his people and be their servant and their father.'

She said, 'Take the sword and the golden shoes. Go to your father, Aegeus, king of Attica, where he lives in Athens. Say to him, "I have moved the rock of Zeus, and these are the things I found under it." Then show him the sword and the golden shoes.'

'But what will you do, my mother, when I have gone?'

She said, 'I shall be here. I shall hear of the great things that you have done, and I shall be happy.'

Periphetes

'I must go down to the sea,' Theseus told himself, 'and get a ship and go to Athens.' Then he thought again. 'But perhaps my father, Aegeus, has other sons in Athens. He may love those sons, but he doesn't know me. He won't be pleased when he sees me. Perhaps he will even send me away.' And then he asked himself, 'How can I make my father want me?—I must do great things so that he will be glad that I am his son.—I won't go to Athens on a ship. I'll go the dangerous way. I'll walk and ride over the hills, and along the rivers, and through the fields and forests. And, as I go, I'll find great things to do. Aegeus will hear of them, and when he knows that I am his son, he'll be glad.'

So Theseus went over fields and through forests and over great open places where there were no trees, and he came to the Hill of Periphetes. There was a way between walls, going up to the top of the hill. The way became narrower and narrower as Theseus went up. When he came to the top, he saw a very big man—a giant—sitting on a hill of round stones. He looked again and saw that they were not stones: they were men's heads! The giant on top of them was dressed in the skin of a bear, and he had a great club in his hand.

Theseus kills Periphetes

'Ah! I see food!' the giant cried. 'I am Periphetes, and I see food walking into my house. Now I shall eat!'

Theseus went nearer.

'Come nearer,' said the giant. 'This is my club. I shall hit you with it and eat you, just as I have eaten many other men. Look. Here are their heads!'

Then he sprang at Theseus and hit at him with the great club—whoosh! The club came down and made a great hole in the place where Theseus had been standing. But Theseus was not there; he had jumped very quickly to one side. He ran at Periphetes with his father's sword and killed him. Then he took the bear-skin and the club and went on down the hill.

When he came down the hill, he saw fields and houses; there were men working in the fields, and women washing clothes in the river, and children playing under the trees. When they saw Theseus, they all ran away. The children ran away and hid in the houses. The men ran into a forest, and the women jumped into the river.

'Why do they all run away?' Theseus wondered. But he sat down near the river and he washed himself in the water. Then he lay down and went to sleep.

A bad country

When he woke up, Theseus heard people talking. He opened his eyes, and he saw some

women looking at him across the little river.
One said, 'He's Periphetes! Look at the bear-
skin and the club. Come away! He'll kill you.'
But the second woman said, 'No! No! That
isn't Periphetes. Periphetes is ugly and terrible,
but this man is beautiful and strong.'

Theseus called out, 'I'm not Periphetes.
Periphetes is dead. I killed him, and this is the
bearskin and the club that I took from him.'

Then they came across the river, and the men
and the children all came and stood near.
Theseus told them how he had killed Periphetes.

Then the women brought him food, and they
sat by the river and sang. They were very
happy because Periphetes was dead. 'Live here
with us,' they said. 'We will give you a house,
a garden and fields.'

But Theseus said, 'I must go on. I must go to
Athens.'

'Are you going to Athens? Are you going
alone? You can't go to Athens alone. It's too
dangerous. There is Sinis: he is a thief who lives
in the forest and kills men. And there is Sciron,
who throws men as food to his fish. And
Kerkyon, who wrestles with every man who
comes; he breaks them in pieces and they die.'

'This is a bad country,' Theseus said, 'and its
king is not a good king. Why are there thieves
and killers on the roads so that men are afraid to
go from place to place? But I must go on.'

Sinis, Sciron, and Kerkyon

Theseus went on and he came to a great forest.
Under the trees he could not see the sun.
Suddenly Sinis sprang out at him from behind a
tree, but Theseus was ready. He had his sword
in his hand, and he cut off the arm of the thief
as he hit at Theseus with his club.

He went on and found a big man sitting on a
great rock beside the sea. The sea was full of big
fish, and the fish were jumping out of the
water: they wanted food.

The big man said, 'Come and sit with me and
look at my fish.' Then he came behind Theseus
and tried to throw him into the water. But
Theseus was too quick for him: he threw back
his hands, pulled the man by the hair, and threw
him into the water. 'There, Sciron!' he called.
'Now you can be food for your own fish!'

Theseus went on and came to the country
where Kerkyon was king. As he went along the
road, a man said, 'Where are you going?'

'I'm going to the house of Kerkyon,' Theseus
answered.

'Why do you want to die? Kerkyon is the
strongest of all men. He will say to you, "Come
and eat with me." And when you have eaten, he
he will say, "Come and wrestle with me." And
he will break you to pieces.'

Theseus said, 'Perhaps he will. Thank you for telling me. But I have wrestled with strong men in my home, and no man has ever thrown me down.'

The wrestling

Theseus came to Kerkyon's house. He went in, and there he saw the king sitting in the hall alone. There was food on the table, and Kerkyon said, 'Come, friend, and eat with me.'

So Theseus sat down, and they ate. When they had eaten, Kerkyon said, 'You have eaten with me, and now you must wrestle with me. We will see who is stronger.'

So they went out into a field. There were many people standing there, and they were saying, 'Look. Kerkyon has found another man to wrestle with him, and he will throw this beautiful man down and kill him.'

Kerkyon and Theseus wrestled in the field. They were both very strong. The sun went down and night came. Suddenly, Kerkyon sprang at Theseus; he wanted to throw him down and fall on him, but Theseus caught Kerkyon and threw him back over his head.

He fell and lay there—dead. Then all the people cried out to Theseus, 'Be our king, and live with us!'

Theseus answered, 'I will be your king, and I will be a friend and a father to you. But now I must go on to Athens, to King Aegeus.'

Procrustes

Theseus went on, and he came to a great hill. There he saw a man dressed in rich clothes. His name was Procrustes. He came to Theseus and said, 'You have walked a long way. Come to my house and eat, and sleep there. You must sleep on the golden bed in my house. You will sleep well on that bed.'

Theseus thought, 'I *have* walked a long way; that's true. And I do need food and sleep. But I don't like this man. He is not good. His eyes make me afraid.' But he said, 'Thank you. I will come.' So they went up the hill.

As they went up, Procrustes looked back. He saw men coming along the road with donkeys carrying things to sell, and a rich man was riding with them on a big horse.

'Ah, poor men!' said Procrustes. 'I'm glad that I looked back and saw them. The nearest house is a long way from here. But I can give them food and beds tonight. I'll go and call them and come back to you.'

Theseus went on up the hill. He saw an old man with a load of wood. He had put the wood

down, and now he was trying to take it up
again and put it on his back, but he couldn't. He
called out to Theseus, 'Please come and help me
with this wood. I'm very old.'

Theseus ran up to the old man. He took the
wood and carried it up the hill.

'Who are you?' asked the old man, walking
by his side. 'And why are you in this unhappy
place? Why are you going up this hill?'

'I'm going up the hill,' said Theseus, 'because
a rich man has asked me to his house to have a
meal with him and to sleep on his golden bed.
I have walked a long way, and I need food and
sleep.'

The golden bed

'Ah!' cried the old man. 'Will Procrustes never
have enough? Don't you know that you are
going to a house of the dead? Procrustes brings
men to his house; he gives them food and,
when they have eaten, he takes them to the
golden bed, and he kills them on it. I was once a
rich man. I went to his house. But when he
came to kill me, I was not asleep. So he made
me his servant. I carry wood and water to the
house. Go! Go now!—But where can you go?
There is no road on from here. Hide—quickly
—hide, and when Procrustes has gone up to his

house you can go back along this road.'

'No,' said Theseus, 'I won't go—and I'm not going to die. This country has a bad king; it is full of thieves. How many bad men must I kill to make this a happy country and save its people?'

He went to the house with Procrustes. They had a meal, and when they had eaten, Procrustes said, 'Now I will lead you to the golden bed so that you may sleep a long sleep.'

They went into the room. Quickly Theseus threw Procrustes on the golden bed. 'Lie there,' he said. 'Tell me, Procrustes, how many men have you killed? How many men, who lay on that bed asleep? Now *you* shall sleep—a long, long sleep.' And he killed Procrustes on the golden bed.

There were boxes and cases of jewels, money and gold in the house. Procrustes had taken these things from the men he had killed. Theseus called the old servant and said to him, 'Give this money back to the people of the country. I must go to Athens, but I will come back, and I will be king. I will be a friend and a father to the people, and I will make them happy.'

To Athens

So Theseus went on to Athens. The people of Athens had heard of the great things that Theseus had done. They came running out of their houses to look at him, and the women threw down flowers in front of him as he walked up to the palace of Aegeus.

Aegeus was the king in Athens, but no one knew that he had a son. His brother Pallas had very many sons, and they all lived in the palace. Medea lived in the palace too. Aegeus was in the power of this terrible woman.

Theseus came to the hall of the palace. He stood at the door and looked. There he saw the sons of Pallas. They were eating, drinking and laughing, and girls were singing to them. But he could not see Aegeus. Aegeus was not in the hall.

The sons of Pallas

'Now I know why this country is unhappy,' Theseus said to himself. 'Now I know why there are thieves and men who kill people to get their money. These sons of Pallas are the real rulers of the country.'

One of the sons of Pallas saw Theseus and called out, 'Hi, you! What do you want?'

'I have come as a friend to see King Aegeus.'

'Come in. Come and drink with us. We like to drink with big strong men.'

'I haven't come to see you, or to drink with you. I have come to see King Aegeus, who is the head of this house.'

They all laughed at this. 'King Aegeus, head of this house! Ha, ha! It is our house. We are all heads of this house.'

'Then it is my house too,' said Theseus, and he came into the hall and looked everywhere for Aegeus.

The sons of Pallas were angry. 'I don't like this man,' one of them said.

'Throw him out of the hall,' cried another.

'You throw him out. He's too big and strong for me.'

So they all sat there, and none of them came to throw Theseus out of the hall.

Then Theseus called one of the servants: 'Go and tell King Aegeus that Theseus of Troezen is here and wants to see him.'

Theseus meets Aegeus

The servant ran and told Aegeus, where he sat in his room with Medea. She was beautiful, but her eyes were like the eyes of a snake.

When Aegeus heard the name 'Troezen', his

face turned white. He stood up and there was fear in his voice as he spoke. 'Theseus? Theseus of Troezen?'

Medea looked at him with her snake-eyes. 'Don't you know who this Theseus is?' she said. 'He is the man who has done great things. But I didn't know that he had come to Athens. We must go out to him and ask him to come in.'

So Aegeus went out into the hall. When Theseus saw his father, he was very happy. He wanted to run to him and say, 'Father, this is your son! I am your son, Theseus.' But he thought, 'Does Aegeus want me? I don't know, so I won't tell him yet that I am his son.' He said, 'King Aegeus, I have saved your people from thieves and killers, and your people are glad. I have come to tell you this, and to say: if there are more bad people in Attica, I'll help you to deal with them too.'

Aegeus looked at him and loved him. He answered sadly, 'I am called "King", but I am not king. I am king in name only. I can't give you anything—gold or jewels. But I can thank you, and I can ask you to eat at my table.'

The king sat down at the table with Theseus at his side, and they ate.

Medea

Medea saw all this. She saw that Aegeus was afraid when he heard the name 'Theseus'. She saw how happy Aegeus was when he saw Theseus. And she saw that Theseus was bigger and stronger than all the sons of Pallas. The sons of Pallas were in her power; she knew that Theseus would never be in her power. 'This man,' she thought, 'will become head of this house; he will be stronger than the sons of Pallas; he will make Aegeus strong—or he may become king in place of Aegeus. Whichever happens, I shall lose my power.'

She went away to her room, where she kept the things that she needed for her magic.

The servants looked at Theseus. They said to each other, 'This is the man who has done such wonderful things. See how strong he is! King Aegeus needs a son—a strong man to help him. Why doesn't King Aegeus have a son as strong as this man?'

Medea came into the hall. She had put on her finest clothes and jewels; she looked very beautiful. In her hand she had a gold cup. She gave the cup to Theseus, saying, 'We thank you, great one, for what you have done for our country. I have made this drink to show our thanks. Please drink it.'

Theseus looked into her eyes, and he saw that they were like the eyes of a snake. He said, 'I thank you, beautiful princess. But you must drink first.'

'I am ill,' she said. 'I must not drink.'

Theseus looked at her again. He said, 'If you don't drink from this cup, I shall kill you.' He drew his sword and stood near her. 'Drink!' he said again.

Medea gave a terrible cry. She threw the cup down and ran out of the hall, and no man ever saw her again.

Aegeus cried, 'That sword! Where did you get that sword? Tell me! Who are you?'

The people of Athens sing

Theseus took out the golden shoes. 'I got the sword in the place where I found these golden shoes.'

Aegeus threw open his arms. 'My son!' he cried. And he said to the sons of Pallas, 'This is my son. He has come to me at last.'

The sons of Pallas said, 'He is not your son. He is a man who has come in out of the street, saying that he is your son.' They drew their swords and ran towards Theseus. But Theseus was stronger than all the sons of Pallas. He began to kill them—easily—and they ran out of the hall into the street. But the people knew them and hated them; nobody tried to save them. Many of them were killed, and the others ran away out of Athens and were never seen again.

Then the people of Athens were very happy. They came up to the king's palace singing: 'Our king will be a king again, and he and his son will love his people and be good to them.'

The man from Crete

Theseus lived with his father and helped him to rule Attica wisely. Days, weeks and months passed, and the people were happy. Then a time came when Theseus saw that they were looking sad.

'Why are you sad?' he asked. But no one answered him.

One day, a man came riding up to the palace. As he rode along the street, the people hid their faces and the women ran into their houses and shut the doors.

'Who are you?' asked Theseus. 'Why are the people afraid of you? Go back to the man who sent you and say, "No man shall come to Athens and make the people of King Aegeus afraid."'

The man answered, 'I have come from the

king of Crete.'

'Why have you come?'

'My king is greater than Aegeus. His army is stronger than the army of Aegeus. So every year the people of Athens must send to my king seven fine boys and seven beautiful girls. These boys and girls have been sent every year to my king in Crete. I have come to get the boys and girls for this year.'

The Labyrinth

Theseus asked his father, 'Is it true? Are boys and girls sent every year to the king of Crete?'

'Yes, they are,' Aegeus answered sadly.

'Do they ever come back?'

'No. Never. They are sent into the Labyrinth. No one can get out of the Labyrinth.'

'What is the Labyrinth?' asked Theseus.

'It is a building in which there are hundreds of passages. You can't get out of it because you don't know where to go. You don't know which passage will lead you out. The Minotaur lives inside the Labyrinth.'

'What is the Minotaur?'

'The Minotaur,' Aegeus answered, 'is half bull and half man, and men are its food. It is terrible, but seven boys and seven girls must go, this year and every year.'

'I see,' said Theseus. 'Yes, they will go. And I'll be one of them.'

So seven girls, six boys and Theseus went down to the ship. The girls were crying. The boys walked with their heads up, saying nothing, but thinking of the terrible place to which they were going.

'Don't be afraid,' said Theseus. 'Is the Minotaur more terrible than the bad men I have killed?'

They looked back at Athens as the ship went out to sea.

'Shall we ever see our homes again?' they said. And the answer seemed to be, 'Never.'

The island of Crete

The ship reached Crete. Theseus, the six boys and the seven girls were led into the hall of the king's palace. The king was sitting there; he looked at them.

'The Minotaur needs food,' he said. 'You must go into the Labyrinth—one by one. Who will go first?'

'I'll go first,' said Theseus.

'Who are you?' asked the king, seeing how big and strong Theseus was.

'I am the son of Aegeus, king of Athens. And I am the last man of Athens who will ever go into the Labyrinth.'

'Why do you say that? There are thirteen others, six boys and seven girls. And there will be fourteen more next year—and every year. Why do you say, "I am the last"?'

'I say it because I have come to kill the Minotaur.'

The king laughed. 'You don't know what you are saying. You haven't seen the Minotaur.' Then he said to his men, 'Lead this foolish young man away. He will go into the Labyrinth tomorrow. He is big and strong— and the Minotaur needs food.'

Ariadne

Ariadne was in the hall, watching. She was the daughter of the king. She saw Theseus and listened to him, and she fell in love with him. She came to the room where Theseus and the others were shut up. She said, 'Look. I have got the key of this room. I'll open the door and let you all out. You can go to my boat and it will take you back to Athens.'

'No,' said Theseus. 'We all thank you, but I have come here to kill the Minotaur, so that no more girls and boys from Athens will ever be put in the Labyrinth.'

'You can't kill the Minotaur,' Ariadne said.

'Nobody can kill him.'

'I'm strong,' Theseus answered.

'If you *do* kill him, you can't get out of the Labyrinth. You'll die there.' She thought for a minute. Then she said, 'I can help you, but my father mustn't know. When you have killed the Minotaur, will you take me with you, back to Athens?'

Theseus looked at Ariadne and loved her. She was so beautiful and so good. 'I will kill the Minotaur,' he said, 'and I'll take you back to Athens with me, and I'll make you my princess and my queen.'

That night, when everyone was asleep, Ariadne came to Theseus. She said, 'Take this sword and hide it in your clothes. Take this thread; it will help you to get out of the Labyrinth—if you live.'

In the Labyrinth

The sun rose, and the king's men came. They led Theseus into the Labyrinth and went away. Theseus went through passage after passage, this way and that. As he went, he put down the thread behind him. Everywhere he went, there was the thread to show him the way back again.

After a long time, he heard something. It was a sound like a great wind—the Minotaur

breathing. He looked, and he took the sword in his hand. He saw a 'thing'—half man, half bull —as big as a house.

At the same time, the Minotaur saw him. It put its head down—as a bull does—and ran at him. Theseus sprang to the side, faster than thought. As the Minotaur went by, the sword went in behind its head. It fell. For a time the great legs kicked. Then it was dead.

Theseus took the thread. It led him back to the door of the Labyrinth.

'Open!' he called. 'The Minotaur is dead.'

Ariadne opened the door.

'I have killed the Minotaur,' he said. Then they ran to the place where the boys and girls were shut in, and opened the door.

Theseus took Ariadne's hand, and they went down to the sea.

Jason and the Golden Fleece

'Bring me the Golden Fleece'

Jason was the son of Aeson, the king of Iolcus.
When Jason was still a baby, Aeson's brother
Pelias made himself king. Jason's mother saved
the child, and Jason grew up far away from
Iolcus.

One day, a fine young man came to see the
king of Iolcus.

'Who are you?' asked Pelias.

'I am Jason, the son of Aeson. He is dead, and
so I am the real king of this country. You must
give me the crown and leave Iolcus.'

Pelias wanted to kill the young man, but he
couldn't because Jason had powerful friends. So
he thought quickly, and then he said, 'Yes. I am
old and tired. You can be king of Iolcus. But
first you must show that you are brave and
strong. You must bring me the Golden Fleece.'

Everybody knew about the Golden Fleece. It
was the magic skin of a golden sheep. And it
was in far-away Colchis, watched by a terrible
dragon.

The Argo and the Argonauts

Jason asked Argus, the best shipbuilder in Greece, to make him a very strong ship with places for fifty men. He asked fifty of the great Greek heroes to come with him. They were great men of war like Theseus and Hercules, great seamen like Tiphys, and the wonderful singer Orpheus. Jason called his ship the *Argo*, and his heroes were the *Argonauts*.

It was a terrible journey, through rough seas and past dangerous rocks and islands. The Sirens sang their magic songs to draw the Argonauts to their death, but Orpheus was a better singer, and the Argonauts listened to him until they had safely passed the danger.

At last they reached Colchis, and Jason went to see the king.

'I have come,' he said, 'to get the Golden Fleece.'

The king of Colchis had a great army and very many strong ships of war. But he was afraid of the Argonauts because he had had a terrible dream about them. He dared not say 'No', but his answer was not just 'Yes'.

'You can have the fleece,' the king said, 'if you plough the great field there and put these dragon's teeth into it as seed. To pull your plough, you must use the two fire-breathing bulls that I shall show you.'

While Jason was thinking about this, the king's daughter came to him. She was Medea (the beautiful but terrible woman who later tried to kill Theseus), and she had fallen in love with Jason.

'I can help you,' she said, 'by my magic. But you must give me your word that you will take me away from here as your wife.'

Medea was very beautiful, and Jason did not know that she and her magic were bad. He said, 'Yes, I'll take you away and make you my wife.'

Medea gave him a liquid to save him from the fire of the bulls' breath. Jason put the liquid on his face and body. Then he wrestled with the two great bulls and made them pull the plough. He ploughed all day and all night. When the field was ready, he put the dragon's teeth into it as seed.

At once the dragon's teeth became soldiers with swords, and they ran towards Jason to kill him. Jason took a round stone and threw it so that it hit two of the soldiers. Each of them thought that the other one had hit him, and they began to fight. Jason threw more stones, and soon all the soldiers were fighting and killing each other. Jason himself killed those who were left alive.

The Argonauts sail away

Then Jason went to the king of Colchis and asked him for the Golden Fleece.

'I never said that you could have the fleece,' the king answered.

That, of course, was not true, so Jason asked Medea to help him to take the fleece.

There was no moon, and the night was very dark, when Medea led Jason and some of his Argonauts to the Golden Fleece. She gave Jason some magic liquid, and he threw it on the dragon. It made the beast move slowly. Jason ran past it, took the fleece, and ran quickly back to the others. The dragon almost caught him, but he threw his shield into its mouth, and it couldn't bite.

Jason and Medea ran with the fleece and their Argonauts to the *Argo*. The other Argonauts had the ship ready, and they sailed quickly away, taking the king's youngest son with them.

'Send all our ships to catch them,' shouted the king. He himself went in the fastest ship.

The terrible Medea saw the king's ships coming close to the *Argo*. She cut the king's youngest son to pieces and dropped the pieces, one by one, into the water. The king ordered his men to take up the pieces, and so the Argonauts sailed away.

The gods were angry because of the boy's death. So the Argonauts had to meet many terrible dangers and great difficulties on the sea and on land. But at last the *Argo* reached Iolcus with the Golden Fleece. While Jason was away, Pelias had built strong walls round his palace, and he had a great army to hold the walls. Jason and the Argonauts couldn't get near him.

'I'll deal with Pelias,' said Medea.

She and Jason went to the palace gates as two old women, and the soldiers let them go in.

'I can make you young again,' Medea said to Pelias. 'But we three must be alone.'

When they were alone, Medea took a knife and seemed to drive it into her own heart, saying some magic words. At once she became young and very beautiful. Jason took the knife, and he too became young and fine-looking.

Medea gave the knife to Pelias, and she seemed to say the same magic words while he drove the knife into his own heart. Pelias died.

Jason went out to the soldiers. They thought that he was Pelias, young again. At his orders, they let the Argonauts come into the palace, and soon Iolcus was his.

Orpheus, the singer

Orpheus and Eurydice

Orpheus had two great loves: he loved his harp, and he loved the beautiful Eurydice. He loved Eurydice most of all.

When he sang and played his harp, all living things came near to hear him. The birds came into the trees over his head; the snakes came out of their holes; the bears came out of the forest; the horses stood and listened in the fields.

Eurydice loved his singing. When he came back from his long journey with the Argonauts, she became his wife.

But one day, when she was walking in the fields, Eurydice put her foot on a snake. The snake bit her. She cried out and fell down. Orpheus ran to her and took her head in his hands. Her eyes were shut. She was dead.

For many days, Orpheus walked over the hills and in the forests, singing sadly because of his lost Eurydice. All living things were sad when they heard him singing.

Orpheus goes to Zeus, and to the country of the dead

At last, Orpheus went to Zeus, the greatest of the gods, and said, 'Eurydice is dead. I don't want to live without her. I want to go into the country of the dead and find Eurydice. If I can't bring her back, I want to stay in the country of the dead with her.'

Zeus saw how sad he was. He heard how sadly and how beautifully he sang. And he said, 'Go, Orpheus. Go to Hades, the king of the dead, and ask him to give her back to you.'

So Orpheus went to the country of the dead. There he saw Charon, the boatman who carries the dead across the River Styx in his boat.

Orpheus said, 'Take me over the river.'

But Charon said, 'I can't take you over the river; you are living. I take the dead across the river, but not the living.'

Then Orpheus sang. When Charon heard him, he couldn't say 'No'. He carried Orpheus across the River Styx to the country of the dead.

On the other side of the river, there was a great gate. A great dog with three terrible heads was sitting there.

'Open the gate, Cerberus,' said Orpheus. 'I want to go into the place of the dead.''

Cerberus answered, 'You are living. I can't

open the gate to the living. I open the gate for the dead, and you are not dead.'

But Orpheus sang, and Cerberus heard him and opened the gate. Orpheus went into the place of the dead.

The place of the dead

First Orpheus saw some of the people who had not led good lives. There was one man standing in water, and trying to drink it. But when he tried to drink, the water ran away. There was an apple tree near him, but he could never reach the apples; they always moved just a little way away from his hand.

Another man had to push a great stone up a hill. He almost got the stone to the top of the hill, but then it fell down again. Then he went down and tried to push it up again. And so it went on, again and again, up—up—and—down! Day after day, year after year—for ever.

Hades, king of the dead

Orpheus came to the house of King Hades. He went into the great hall, where Hades sat with his queen, Persephone. Queen Persephone goes up every year into the country of the living. When she is there, the sun becomes hot; the days are long; flowers come out in the gardens; apples grow on the trees, and the birds sing. When Persephone goes back to the place of the dead, everything dies, and men sit in their houses near the fire.

Orpheus said, 'O King Hades and Queen Persephone, please give me back Eurydice.' And he sang very sadly, telling them how much he loved Eurydice and how much he wanted to be with her.

Then Hades said, 'Go back, Orpheus, and Eurydice shall walk behind you. But don't speak to her as you go. Don't look back at her. If you give one look, she will fall back into the place of the dead, and you will never see her again.'

Orpheus looks back

Then Orpheus began his journey back to the country of the living. As he walked, he sang about his love for Eurydice. And as he walked, he heard Eurydice walking behind him, and his heart was full of happiness. The great dog Cerberus opened the gate to him, and he came to the River Styx. He sat in the front of Charon's boat, and he heard Eurydice get in behind him. They went across the river and began to walk—up—up—towards the sun.

As they came near the country of the living, and Orpheus saw the sun in front of him, he wondered, 'Is Eurydice as beautiful as she was when I used to sing to her?'

He looked back at her.

She gave a little cry—and she had gone!

Orpheus could not go to bring her back. He walked over hills, by the side of rivers and in forests, singing sadly.

At last he died. He came to the River Styx, and Charon carried him across. 'You are dead,' he said. 'Now I can carry you.'

The great dog Cerberus opened the gate and he went into the place of the dead, and there he saw Eurydice—as beautiful as she was when he used to sing to her in the country of the living. He took her hand, and they walked through the gardens and fields, where the good men go when they die, and all are happy for ever.

Ulysses and the one-eyed Cyclops

The wooden horse

For ten years the Greeks tried to take the city of Troy, but the walls of the city were strong and the people of Troy fought well. At last the Greeks built a great horse made of wood. They hid soldiers inside it. Then all the other Greeks went away.

The people of Troy saw the horse.

'What is that wooden horse?' they asked each other. 'Shall we bring it into the city? We can open the gate of the city now, because the Greeks have gone away. We must see what that wooden horse is.'

So they opened the gate of Troy and went out and brought the wooden horse into the city.

At night, the men came out from the horse. They fought their way to the gate and opened it. The other Greeks had come back, and they ran in and took the city.

The cave

After that, the Greeks left Troy and began the long journey back to Greece. Ulysses was one of

the Greek leaders. He and his men went on to
their ship.

After many days, they came to an island.
They needed food and water, so they stopped
and went on to the island. They found a great
cave, and Ulysses went into it with his men.

Inside the cave he saw a great deal of food,
but there was no one in the cave. Ulysses said,
'The man is working in the field. He will come
back when the sun goes down. We'll wait in the
cave and ask him to help us.'

Cyclops comes to the cave

The sun went down. Ulysses looked out and he
saw a giant coming back to the cave. The
giant, Cyclops, was as big as six men. He had
one big eye. He was carrying a tree to put on
his fire.

He drove his goats—very big goats—into the
cave. Then he himself came into the cave and
closed the opening with a great rock. He made
a fire. He took the milk from his goats. Then he
looked up, with his one big eye, and saw
Ulysses and his men.

'Who are you?' he said. 'What is your name?
Are you a thief, or have you come to buy and
sell?'

'We are not thieves,' said Ulysses, 'and we

haven't come to buy and sell. We are soldiers, and we are coming back from the city of Troy. We ask you to give us food and a place to sleep.'

'Where is your ship?' asked the giant.

Ulysses thought, 'If Cyclops finds our ship, he may break it. Then we'll never get away from the island.' So he said, 'We have no ship. It went down in the sea.'

Cyclops did not answer, but he took two of the men and killed them. Then he ate them. He drank a great pot of milk, and after that he lay down and slept.

Caught in the cave

Ulysses thought. 'We must get out of this cave. But how? Shall I kill Cyclops in his sleep? No. I mustn't do that because the opening is closed with that great rock and we can't move it. We'll be shut in here with a dead Cyclops, and that will be terrible. But while Cyclops is alive, he'll eat us, two men every day. We must get out of the cave, but how?' He thought hard, and at last he said, 'I know what I must do.'

When Cyclops went out of the cave in the morning, he closed the opening with the great rock. There was a long stick in the cave. It was part of a tree, and very strong. Ulysses took his axe and cut the end of the stick to a point.

When the sun went down, Cyclops came back to the cave. He drove his goats into the cave. Then he put back the great rock across the opening of the cave. He made a fire. Then he took the goats' milk.

Ulysses had some strong drink that he had brought from the ship. He went to Cyclops and said, 'Don't drink milk. Drink this. You will like it: it's nice.'

Cyclops drank it. 'Yes,' he said. 'It's good.'

'No Man'

Ulysses said, 'Cyclops, yesterday you asked my name. My name is No Man. Drink some more of this.'

Cyclops drank, and then he fell asleep.

When Cyclops was asleep, Ulysses pushed the stick hard into the giant's one eye. Cyclops jumped up with a terrible cry. Cry after cry came from him as he tried to find Ulysses. He wanted to kill the Greek.

There were some other giants like Cyclops living in caves on the island. They all came running and stood outside the cave.

'What's the matter?' they called. 'Why are you crying out? Has a thief taken your goats? Or is some man hurting you?'

'No Man is hurting me!' Cyclops cried. 'No Man!'

Then the other giants said, 'Don't cry out when no man is hurting you.' And they went back to their caves.

Under the goats

When he thought that day had come, Cyclops moved the rock from the opening of the cave. He could not see, but he sat down in the opening and put out his hands. He thought, 'The goats must go out to the field, but No Man and his men mustn't go. I'll feel the goats' backs with my hands, and so I'll know that they are goats, and I'll let them go out. But if I feel a man, I'll kill him, and I'll kill every man who comes under my hands.'

Ulysses was watching Cyclops. He saw what the giant was doing, and he said to his men, 'Go out under the goats.'

So the men got under the goats, one man under each goat, holding on to the goat's skin. Cyclops felt the back of each goat and thought, 'Ah! That's a goat, not a man.' And he let the goat pass. He did not know that there was a man under it. So Ulysses and his men got out of the cave safely.

The Greeks ran to their ship. Cyclops heard

them running, and he ran after them, feeling his way. As the ship left, he heard it, and he threw great stones at it. One stone fell in front of the ship so that the ship was carried back to the island. Cyclops heard it and threw another great stone. That stone fell behind the ship and sent it out to sea again. He went on throwing stones, but now the ship was far away and he could not hit it.

So Ulysses and his men were saved. Many other things happened to them on their journey, but at last they reached their homes in Greece.

Atalanta, the runner

The fastest runner

Atalanta was the daughter of a king. She was very beautiful, very strong, and she could run very fast. She could run faster than any man in any country. And she could shoot so well that (some people say) she went to Colchis with the Argonauts.

But she did not want to marry. 'I couldn't be happy as a wife,' she said. 'I want to run over the hills. I want to run faster than the fastest horse; I want to run faster than birds can fly. There is no man I want to marry.'

Her father said, 'You *must* marry. Say what man you will marry. Will you marry a king?— or a prince?—or a great hero?'

Atalanta thought. Then she said, 'I will marry a man who can run faster than I can. When a man says that he wants to make me his wife, I'll run with him. I'll marry the man who runs faster than I can, but you must kill any man who can't.'

Hippomenes goes to Aphrodite

Atalanta was so very beautiful that many princes and great men came. A man called Hippomenes saw them getting ready to run. He had never seen Atalanta. He wondered, 'Why do they do this foolish thing? Do they want to be killed because they can't run as fast as a woman?'

Then Atalanta came out of the house to run. He saw how beautiful she was. He said, 'If I can't marry Atalanta, I'll die.'

He saw the other men run. Some of them ran very fast. But Atalanta was like a bird flying. The men were left far behind.

Hippomenes asked himself, 'How can I run as fast as Atalanta? How can I be first when I run with her?'

He went to Aphrodite, the goddess of love. Hippomenes found Aphrodite sitting in her garden. He said, 'I love Atalanta, and I want to marry her. She will marry the man who can run faster than she can—no other man. How can I win when I run with her? Help me, Aphrodite. You are the goddess of love, and I love. I love Atalanta.'

Aphrodite said, 'Yes, I will help you.'

She took three golden apples from the tree in her garden and gave them to Hippomenes. She

said, 'Throw an apple in front of Atalanta when
she is running. She will stop to get it. You must
run on, and so you may win.'

Atalanta and the golden apples

Hippomenes took the three golden apples and
went to the king, Atalanta's father.

'I want to marry Atalanta,' he said.

'Foolish young man,' the king said, 'do you
know what you are doing? Many men have
wanted to marry her, but they couldn't run
faster than she can, so they are dead. Do you
want to die?'

Hippomenes answered, 'If I can't marry
Atalanta, I *will* die!'

So the next day, Hippomenes went out to the
field and stood there. Atalanta came out from
the house. She looked at Hippomenes, and she
thought, 'I don't want this man to die. He is
beautiful, brave and good.' To her father she
said, 'Tell him to go away. I don't want to run
with him.'

But Hippomenes said, 'She has said that she
will marry the man who runs faster than she
can. Come now! Run!'

Atalanta ran. Hippomenes ran. He was the
fastest runner of all the men in that country. But
Atalanta ran faster. She was soon in front of

him, and he was far behind.

Then Hippomenes threw one of the golden apples. It went over Atalanta's head and fell in front of her. She stopped and took it up—but Hippomenes ran on. Atalanta was behind him now. She looked up; she saw him in front, and she ran faster than the fastest bird. She was near him. She was in front of him. Soon he was behind her again—far behind.

He threw another apple, over her head, and it fell at her feet. She stopped. She took it up and looked at it—a beautiful golden apple. She hid it in her clothes with the other apple. But Hippomenes had run on. He was in front.

The third apple

Atalanta ran again. Again she left Hippomenes behind her.

Hippomenes thought, 'I have one more golden apple. I won't throw it over her head; I'll throw it to the side. If she turns to the side to get it, I shall win, and—oh, what happiness!— she will be my wife. But if she sees it and *doesn't* turn, then she will win—and I'll die.'

He threw the apple. It did not fall in front of Atalanta but to the side. She saw it. She thought, 'I won't turn to get that golden apple. If I do, he will run on and win.' But then she

thought, 'He is brave, beautiful and good, and I don't want him to die.' She turned and took up the apple.

Hippomenes ran on. He was tired, and he was not running fast now. Atalanta saw him in front, and she thought, 'Poor man! I can run now, like a bird flying, and leave him far behind. But I don't want to do that.'

She ran on, but she didn't run very fast. Hippomenes won.

Hippomenes married Atalanta. Some people who tell the story say that Hippomenes did not thank Aphrodite for her help, and so she changed him and Atalanta into a lion and lioness in the forest. But others say that he did thank Aphrodite, and that they lived happily ever after.

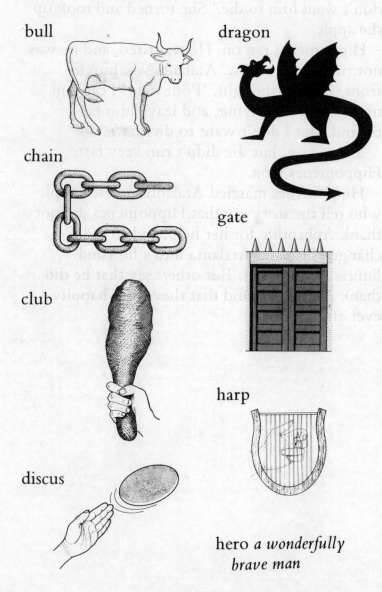

List of extra words

bull

dragon

chain

gate

club

harp

discus

hero *a wonderfully brave man*

lion, lioness

snake

terrible *very bad,*
frightening, or very
dangerous

plough

thread

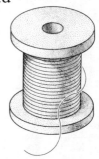

shield

wings

skin *the outside of a*
person's or animal's
body

wrestle *Two men*
wrestle when each
tries to throw the
other to the ground.